Easter Parade

To Emma, who made a great little bunny
—L.M.

ISBN 0-439-65113-1

Words and music by Irving Berlin. Copyright © 1933 by Irving Berlin.
Copyright renewed © 1960 by Irving Berlin. All rights reserved.
Published by Scholastic Inc., 557 Broadway, New York, NY 10012, by arrangement with HarperCollins Publishers.
SCHOLASTIC and associated logos are trademarks and/or registered trademarks of Scholastic Inc.

12 11 10 9 8 7 6 5 4 3 2 1   4 5 6 7 8 9/0

Printed in the U.S.A.   40

First Scholastic printing, March 2004

Typography by Jeanne L. Hogle

Easter Parade

By Irving Berlin ✧ Illustrated by Lisa McCue

SCHOLASTIC INC.

New York Toronto London Auckland Sydney
Mexico City New Delhi Hong Kong Buenos Aires

Never saw you look
Quite so pretty before;
Never saw you dressed
Quite so lovely, what's more,

I could hardly wait
  To keep our date
    This lovely Easter morning,
      And my heart beat fast
        As I came through the door,
          For . . .

In your Easter bonnet

With all the frills upon it

You'll be the grandest lady
In the Easter Parade.

I'll be all in clover

And when they look you over

I'll be the proudest fellow

In the Easter Parade.

On the Avenue, Fifth Avenue,

The photographers will snap us,

And you'll find that you're in the rotogravure.

Oh, I could write a sonnet

About your Easter bonnet

And of the girl I'm taking to
The Easter Parade.

Easter Parade

Words and Music by
IRVING BERLIN

Nev-er saw you look   Quite so pret-ty be - fore;_____   Nev-er saw you dressed   Quite so love-ly, what's